Usborne Wipe-clean

All you Need to Know
Before you
Start School

Activity Book

Written by Holly Bathie and Jessica Greenwell

Illustrations by Marina Aizen

Designed by Frankie Allen

My name is Carla Cat.

My name is Rani Rabbit.

I'm Maddy Mouse.

You could write your own name here, if you want to:

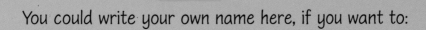

Are we ready for school?

Before we can go to school, we need to finish getting dressed. Can you help us? Draw lines to match each of us to something we want to put on.

What clothes will you wear to school?

Circle three things Rani needs to put in her school bag.

necklace

snack

Rani

water bottle

teapot

reading book

Draw lines from the weather pictures to the things Carla will need on...

...a rainy day

...a sunny day

...a snowy day

What's the weather like where you are today?

sunscreen

mittens

umbrella

sunhat

coat

warm hat

boots

scarf

3

How do we get to school?

We all travel to school in different ways.
Draw lines to match the animals to the right pictures.

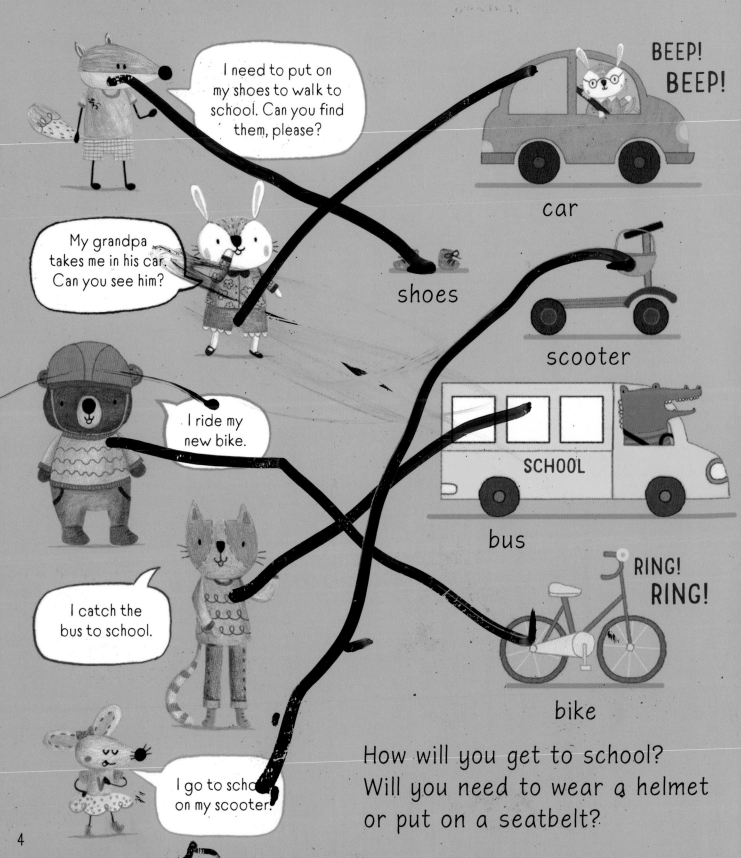

At the pegs

When we get to school, we hang up our things on our pegs. Can you help us, please? Draw lines to match the bags to the pegs. Then, trace over the shapes.

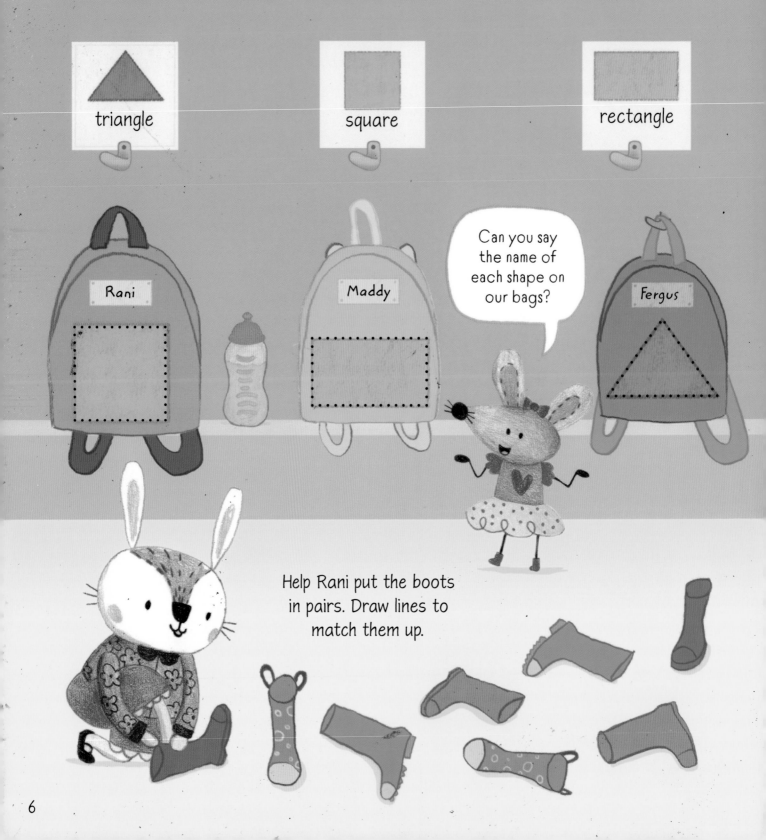

triangle

square

rectangle

Rani

Maddy

Can you say the name of each shape on our bags?

Fergus

Help Rani put the boots in pairs. Draw lines to match them up.

Who's here?

Help Mr. Honeybear take attendance. Trace over the numbers and letters and add a check mark for each animal in class today.

Mr. Honeybear needs 5 of each of the things below for the 5 animals in his class. Draw 1 more of each thing to make 5.

Can you help me count how many of each thing I have?

1 more paint bottle

1 more ball

1 more block

1 more book bag

Classroom fun

There are lots of fun things to do in our classroom.
Use your pen to join in with our games and activities.

Draw a picture for the art wall here.

Count the flags on
the playhouse.

Draw lines to
connect each set
of dots on the
playhouse.

Trace over the tangled strings to see who will play with each toy.

Trace over these letters.

11

It's playtime!

We love playing outside at school. Trace over
all the dotted lines to finish this picture.

Time for PE

Trace over the lines to show some ways we can move our bodies in PE.

I can jump up and down.

I can run really fast.

I've just learned how to hop!

I can twirl around and around.

One... two... three... These balls are so bouncy!

Circle the smallest ball.
Put a dot on the biggest ball.

Art lesson

Fergus has painted a lovely, splotchy picture. Draw a line from each bottle of paint to match one of the splotches.

You can doodle on our picture with your black pen if you want.

red   blue   yellow   green

purple   orange   pink   gray

Can you name each shape and color?

Bertie has cut out lots of shapes. Circle the odd one out in each row.

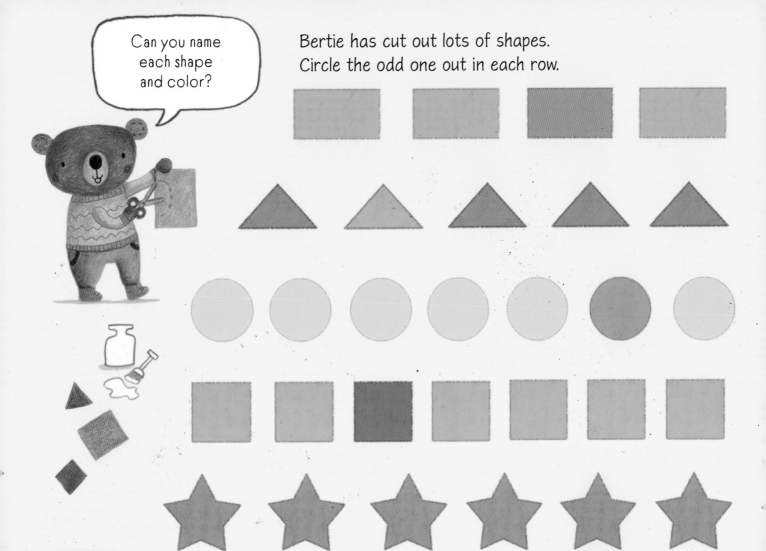

Can you circle 5 differences in Carla's train pictures?

My pictures look so similar but they're not quite the same!

Choo, choo!

What's for lunch?

What's on the menu today? Choose something for each animal to eat and copy it onto the plate.

Menu

pizza

beans

fish

pasta

peas

carrots

potatoes

I love pizza!

I've brought my lunch from home in my lunchbox.

Add some patterns to the napkins.

Circle the odd one out in each pile of fruit.

apples

pears

bananas

Draw lines on my friends' cups to fill them with water, please.

I'm hungry!

You could wipe the plates clean and draw something else if you want.

Forest school counting

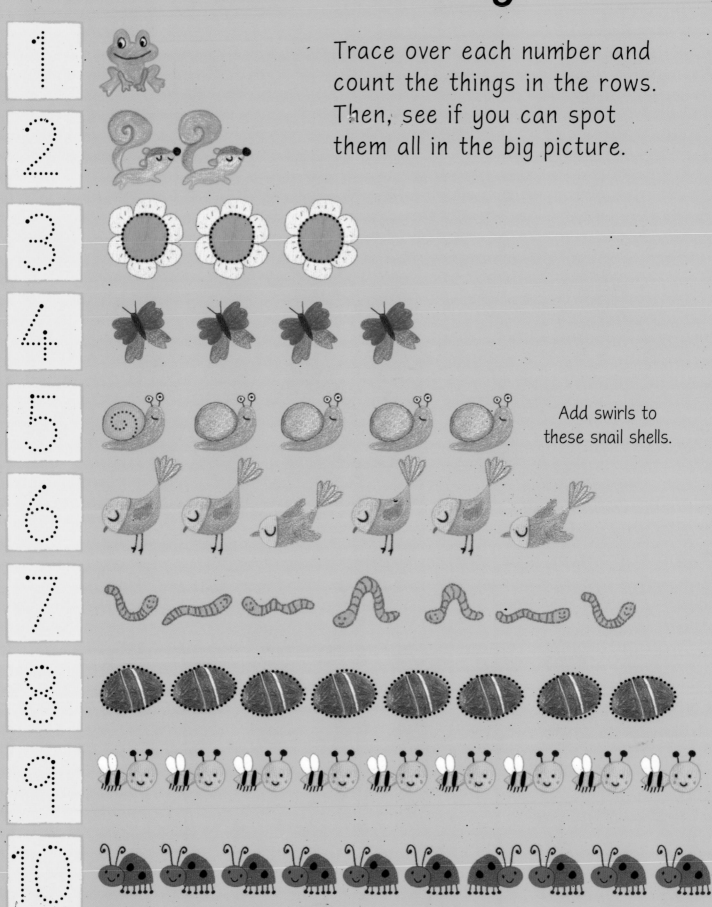

Trace over each number and count the things in the rows. Then, see if you can spot them all in the big picture.

Add swirls to these snail shells.

Put a dot on each thing as you count it.

I've found a pretty pebble on the ground.

Trace around the flowers.

19

Lots of little letters

Choose a picture and circle it with your pen. Say its name and then spot the letter it begins with on the opposite page. You can do as many as you like.

apple

duck

tree

sun

necklace

digger

umbrella

bird

zig-zag

yo-yo

tent

gate

elephant

leaf

octopus

flower

windmill

house

pear

invitation

jar

kite

Now see if you can copy the
letters onto the little lines.

Can you find the
letter my name
begins with?

a_ b_ c_

d_ e_ f_ g_ h_

i_ j_ k_ l_ m_

n_ o_ p_ q_ r_

s_ t_ u_ v_ w_

I can see
my letter.

Can you find
your letter?

x_ y_ z_

Hometime

At the end of the day we take our things home with us.
We have written our names on our pictures.
Can you write them too?

What did we do today?

It's been a busy day at school. Can you remember what we did? Match the pictures to the animals. (You can look back through the book if you need to.)

Who painted this picture?

Who took attendance?

Who goes to school by bike?

Who brought lunch in a lunchbox?

Who played with a red car in the classroom?

Who was looking at sunflowers?

Who found a pretty pebble in the forest?

Who goes to school by scooter?

Who has a bag with a square on it?

Bye-bye and see you again tomorrow!

Bertie   Carla   Maddy   Rani   Fergus   Mr. Honeybear

23

All the letters

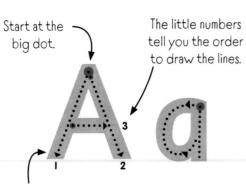

Start at the big dot.

The little numbers tell you the order to draw the lines.

Follow the arrows.

Follow me.

A a B b C c

G g H h I i

M m N n O o

S s T t U u

Y y Z z

Do you know the names of these letters?